VOICE for LIFE

CW00742060

SINGER'S WORKBOOK 4: RED LEVEL

CONTENTS

This book belongs to

_____

of

_____ choir.

Project editor: Tim Ruffer
Written and edited by Catherine Duffy, Anthony Marks and Leah Perona–Wright
This edition fully revised and updated by Anthony Marks

Voice for Life was developed by Leah Perona–Wright in consultation with experienced practitioners from across the UK and beyond. These include Gordon Appleton, Colin Baldy, Roger Brice, Chris Broughton, Lesley Cooper, June Cox, Colin Davey, Paul Ellis, Peter Futcher, Susan Gardner, Ameral Gunson, John Harper, Esther Jones, Sally Leeming, Hilary Llystyn Jones, Sue Moore, David Ogden, Jon Payne, Keith Roberts, Sheila Robertson, Ben Saunders, John Wardle, Alistair Warwick, Geoff Weaver and Jenevora Williams. We are grateful for their contributions.

Design and layout: Anthony Marks and Catherine Duffy
Music origination: Leah Perona–Wright and Anthony Marks
Illustrations: Hilary Perona–Wright
Editorial assistance: Julian Elloway and Sally Ruffer

Printed in Great Britain by Caligraving Ltd, Thetford

ISBN 978–0–85402–214–4

THE ROYAL SCHOOL OF CHURCH MUSIC
19 The Close, Salisbury, Wiltshire, SP1 2EB
Tel: +44 (0)1722 424848   Fax: +44 (0)1722 424849
E-mail: education@rscm.com Website: www.rscm.com
Registered charity no. 312828

Distributed exclusively in North America by GIA Publications, Inc.
7404 S. Mason Ave., Chicago, IL 60638
Toll free: 800 442 1358   Website: www.giamusic.com

Welcome to *Voice for Life*. It is designed to help you discover what your voice can do, and then strengthen it. It will encourage you to learn about music and look at what it means to be a singer and a member of a choir.

This workbook will help you to practise singing and think about music at home, but you will also work closely with your choir trainer. Together you will discuss which topic to work on next – don't try to complete the whole book on your own in one week! Your choir trainer may want to explain a new topic before you go further through the book, or to talk to you at rehearsals about things you should do on your own. He or she may also want to check that you have understood something before you move on to the next stage.

To make the most of your voice, you need to practise regularly. This workbook contains breathing and singing exercises to use at home. If you practise on your own as well as with your choir, you will quickly improve the strength of your voice. As a singer, your whole body is your musical instrument – you take it to bed, on the bus, in the car, shopping, to parties and even on holiday – so it makes sense to take care of all aspects of it. To help you look after your voice, there are tips on voice care throughout the book.

This workbook contains puzzles and exercises to complete in your own time. You will also be expected to talk to other members of your choir to find the answers to some of the questions. Don't worry about doing this – other choir members expect to be asked for information or advice.

Being in a choir is different from being a solo singer. You are a member of a team. You will learn about being a good team member and making the best contribution you can to your choir – at Red level, this includes taking more responsibility for for members of the choir who have less experience than you do.

To complete the Red level of *Voice for Life*, you must achieve the targets listed on pages 40–43. Some targets are about your progress during choir rehearsals, services and concerts; others are about things you will do in your own time. As you work through them, you will improve as a singer and choir member. After you complete each one, your choir trainer will sign its box. You can find out what happens when you complete all the targets inside the back cover. There is a reference section on pages 44–46 and an index on pages 47–48.

Enjoy *Voice for Life!*

Lindsay Gray

Lindsay Gray
Director, RSCM

Icons The icons in this book tell you to:

 Read this before going further

 Try a vocal or physical exercise

 Sing something

 Think about something

 Write an answer in the box

 Tick when you have finished an activity

Posture

Singing is a physical activity, and your voice is your musical instrument. All the muscles in your body are involved in making your musical instrument work. If your muscles are tense, the quality of your voice will be affected. This is why it is important to maintain a good posture in order to sing well. Whether sitting or standing, when your posture is good:

- your body will feel well–balanced and stable, but relaxed

- you will be able to see your conductor clearly at all times

- you will look professional and confident, creating a good impression for your listeners

Imagine you were helping new singers with their posture. To encourage them, you would point out things that are good about the way they stand or sit. But if their posture was not so good, you could mention ways they could improve, and say how a particular way of sitting or standing might affect their singing.

Here is a list of ten things that people often do when they stand or sit to sing. Four of them are good and six of them are bad. Put a tick by the ones that are good and a cross by the ones that are bad.

1 Shoulders raised	6 Weight on one leg
2 Knees locked	7 Knees relaxed
3 Feet firmly on the ground	8 Straight back
4 Music held very high	9 Legs crossed
5 Music held very low	10 Feet slightly apart

Some of the singers below are sitting or standing well – others not so well. Can you spot the good and bad points? Mark each picture with a number from the list above. Take care – some pictures may need more than one number, and you may need to use some numbers more than once.

Now imagine you had to explain to these singers what is good and bad about their posture. Each of these boxes contains something that happens if you do one of the ten numbered things in the list on the opposite page. Which box matches which number? Write the number next to each box. Two of them have been done for you already.

Causes tension in the neck, throat and jaw ◯

(3) Means your whole body is properly supported from the ground up

Sound goes straight down to the floor ◯

Puts the body off-balance, causing tension in the legs, back and neck muscles ◯

◯ Causes tension in the legs which moves through the body, restricting breathing

◯ Music covers your mouth and stifles the sound

◯ Balances your weight and eliminates tension

Makes the body twist and may cause you to slump, restricting your breathing

◯ Means you are sitting or standing upright so your breathing is unrestricted

◯ Means there is not too much tension in your legs **(7)**

Any tension in your body while you are singing will be heard in your voice. The key areas where tension may develop are the jaw, neck and shoulders. If you feel tension building up in your muscles, use the exercises below to help you relax. You can also use them to warm up before you practise singing at home.

Warming up the body and face muscles

- Tense all your muscles, clenching your hands into fists and hunching up your shoulders up. Hold for a few seconds, then relax. Repeat several times.

- Roll your shoulders, one at a time, then both together, in either direction. Roll your head slowly on your neck, opening your mouth as you reach the top so as not to strain your neck.

- Tense up your facial muscles tightly, then open your mouth and eyes as wide as possible, before slowly letting them relax completely.

- Reach up slowly with your hands and arms and then stretch upwards until you are on tiptoes. Then curl the spine slowly downwards, hanging the head and neck, with hands and arms towards the floor. Hang there for a few moments, swaying gently from side to side. Then straighten up to a good upright standing posture.

- Move your jaw round and round or pretend you are chewing a toffee.

- Shake your hands by your side, as though shaking off water.

Breathing

 Your lungs, like your muscles, need exercising so that they can work more efficiently. The following pages explain what happens in your body when you breathe. Understanding this will help you understand how to exercise and develop the muscles and organs that you use for breathing.

The diaphragm

The diaphragm (say 'DYE–a–fram') is a large muscular partition that separates the top half of the body (the chest and lungs) from the bottom half (the abdomen). It is attached to the lower ribs and falls and rises as you breathe.

The diaphragm is the main muscle you use when you breathe in. It draws air into the lungs, providing oxygen to the blood. (You can't actually feel your diaphragm – you feel the muscles around it moving.)

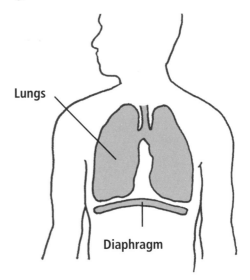

What happens when you breathe

When you breathe in, your diaphragm flattens. This pulls the bottom of the lungs down, which makes air rush down your windpipe into your lungs. As your lungs fill with air, they get bigger. Your lower ribs rise slightly, and your waistline gets wider.

When you breathe out, your diaphragm relaxes again, and the muscles in your abdomen push it back to its natural dome–shaped position. This forces air back out of your lungs. Your lungs get smaller again and your waistline gets narrower.

 Can you label this diagram with the words below?

Diaphragm   Lungs

Windpipe

Waistline

Which way does your diaphragm move when you breathe in?

When you breathe out, do your lungs get bigger or smaller?

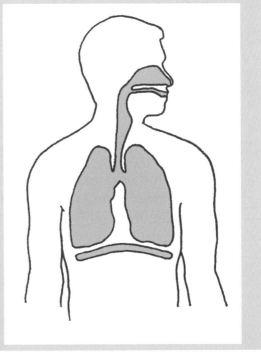

 Another word for breathing in is *inhaling*. Another word for breathing out is *exhaling*. If you put your hands gently on your lower ribs, stomach or waist, and breathe slowly, you will feel your muscles moving around your diaphragm. Remember though that you can't feel the diaphragm itself.

Practising breathing

Although the diaphragm plays such an important part in your breathing, it is not possible to feel it or control it directly. It is the abdominal muscles that surround the diaphragm that will help you to manage your breathing when you sing.

As your breathing is so dependent on muscles working efficiently, you should aim to practise your breathing regularly. Try exercising for about ten minutes a day. This is an ideal way to strengthen your muscles. Here are some exercises to help you.

Keeping a steady upper body

Use this exercise to help you feel the movements in the body that happen when you breathe. Exhale (breathe out), making a 'sss' sound or a whispered 'ah' until your lungs are empty. Can you feel the lower part of your rib cage contract (get smaller) while you do this? Now inhale (breathe in) deeply through your nose and feel how the rib cage naturally moves back out.

Do this again. This time, as you exhale, raise your arms almost as high as your shoulders – but take care not to raise your shoulders themselves. Then, lower your arms as you inhale. While you do this, your upper body should move as little as possible. Remember this feeling of having a steady upper body and keep it when you sing. Otherwise, the upper body tends to collapse towards the end of a phrase. This has a bad effect on the tone.

Exercising the diaphragm

For this exercise, make a barking sound like a dog, or a short laughing 'ha' sound. The sound should be sudden and high-pitched. Repeat it five times. As you do this, you will be able to feel how the diaphragm rapidly contracts and releases.

Comparing relaxed and tense breathing

Drop your jaw slowly. Can you feel how this causes air to be drawn into your lungs? Note how the diaphragm falls and the lower rib cage expands. Do the same thing again, but this time breathe in noisily. This time, your body and diaphragm will become tense, especially the muscles in your neck.

When you take a breath before singing, you should aim to breathe silently to avoid tension in your throat and body. Breathe calmly and deeply, giving yourself plenty of time before you are due to start singing. This means you will have to look and think ahead.

VOICE CARE TIP
Did you know that if you hold your hands behind your back when you sing this will restrict your breathing? When singing without music, keep your hands relaxed and down by your side. This allows your rib cage to move freely.

Breathing

The following exercises will help you to develop your breath control. Try to sing straight through without taking any breaths. If you can't get to the end of each one without taking a breath, don't worry. If you keep practising the exercises on the previous page a little each day, you will gradually find it easier to control your breathing. You will be able to get a little bit further through each time.

Breath control exercises

While singing this exercise, imagine you are inflating a tyre in your lower back – you need to keep 'inflating' right to the end.

mee meh mah maw moo _____   mee meh mah maw moo _____   mee meh mah maw moo _____

mee meh mah maw   moo _____   mee meh mah maw   moo _____

When you are comfortable with the exercise above, try the next one, which will help breath control over a wider range of notes.

mee meh mah maw moo _____   mee meh mah maw moo _____

mee meh mah maw moo _____   mee meh mah maw moo _____

mee meh mah maw moo _____   mee meh mah maw moo _____

Remember that if you feel dizzy or weak while exercising your voice, you should stop, sit down and relax. If the problem continues, talk to your choir trainer.

VOICE CARE TIPS

Did you know that tiredness affects your voice? When you are tired you need more effort to breathe and to speak – this can lead to vocal strain. Tiredness also makes the throat drier. This makes the voice sound strained and lacking in resonance. Try to have some rest before you sing and make sure you drink plenty of water.

Did you know that you need to be reasonably fit in order to sing well? To help improve your stamina for singing, consider taking some form of regular exercise. Running, cycling, aerobics or swimming are all good forms of aerobic exercise, but there are many other sporting activities that will help to keep your heart and lungs healthy. Anything that keeps you active for around 20 minutes is good.

To have the stamina to sing for long periods, it is important to eat little and often. If you have not eaten a proper meal before you sing, eating an energy bar half an hour before you sing will help keep your energy levels up during your rehearsal or performance.

Module A: Using the voice well

Knowing when to breathe

Part of learning how to manage your breath is knowing when you should breathe in a piece of music. There are some general rules that will help you decide when it is suitable to breathe. The most important thing is that your breathing should make sense of the words, so you need to look carefully at the text you are singing to decide when to take a breath.

 It may help to read the text out loud before singing it, so that you know from the sense of the words when to breathe. It may also help to discuss the meaning of the words with other choir members, or your choir trainer. Here are a few more hints to help you decide:

- It is usually best to breathe when you see a comma or full stop in the text.

- You don't need to breathe at every comma – if you carry on without breathing, this makes a longer, smoother phrase.

- Never breathe in the middle of a word (unless you are 'staggering' your breathing – see page 10).

 Look at the music below. There are breath marks throughout the piece (shown as little tick or check marks above the stave). Some of the breath marks are in sensible places, but others are not. Circle the breath marks that you think are correct.

 Not all musicians have the same views about when it is best to breathe in a piece of music. However, when your choir trainer or conductor asks you to breathe (or not to breathe) in a particular place, he or she is trying to achieve a particular musical effect, which only works if all the singers follow the instructions.

Ask your choir trainer to check your answers to the last exercise. Then look at the music below.

This time there are no breath marks. Use the breath mark symbol shown in the last exercise to mark in the places where you think it is appropriate to breathe.

When you have put breath marks into the music, try singing it yourself. Think about the questions below.

- Do you think you have placed the breath marks in the best places?

- Do you need to take all the breaths that you have marked?

Staggered breathing

Sometimes it may not be possible to get through a phrase that your choir trainer has asked you to sing in one breath. Staggered breathing is a way of 'cheating' within a choir to create an illusion of a long phrase being sung with no breaths at all. Each singer takes a quiet breath at a different time from the person next to them – this way the sound keeps going throughout the phrase without a break.

When you stagger your breathing, don't pronounce consonants at the end of the words. Otherwise, it will be obvious that you have taken a breath because your consonant will sound at a different time from everyone else in the choir. (In particular, watch out for 's' and 'c' sounds – they are especially obvious.)

When you speak or sing, the sound you produce comes from your **larynx**. Inside your larynx are your **vocal folds**. As they vibrate, sound is produced.

You can feel these vibrations when you use your voice, and may be able to feel your larynx move upwards as you swallow.

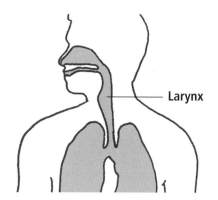

Larynx

The vibrations made by your vocal folds are amplified by other parts of your body. This is called resonating. The vibrations of your vocal folds resonate through your body, especially the hollow parts of your head and upper body.

 Hum a note in the middle of your range. At the same time, touch different areas of your face, neck and throat. Which parts can you feel vibrating and resonating? List them on the right.

Can you feel the sound as it resonates in other parts of your body too? List these as well.

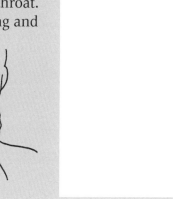

 Producing a resonant sound
Sound resonates in hollow spaces, so one way to produce a resonant sound is to create as much space inside your mouth as possible. Opening your mouth wide as you sing helps. But there is another way of creating space in your mouth. At the back of your mouth is an area of soft tissue called the **soft palate**. If you raise this while you sing, it will help you produce a more resonant sound.

 Finding the soft palate
With your tongue, feel the roof of your mouth. The hard part near the front is called the hard palate. Further back there is an area of soft muscle tissue called the soft palate. If you yawn, you can feel the soft palate rising, creating a space at the back of your mouth. Singing with the soft palate raised allows the sound to resonate more fully. One way to raise your soft palate without yawning is to imagine your back molar teeth lifting up into your head. Practise this and remember how it feels.

 Experimenting with the soft palate
Sing a note in the middle of your range with an 'n' sound and with your lips slightly apart. Use your hands to feel the sound resonating in your throat, mouth, neck and chest. Focus the resonance in your nose and head and feel it buzzing there.

 Take a breath, sing the note again with the 'n' sound, and now raise the soft palate. Then open your mouth and sing 'ee'. Can you hear how much brighter and stronger the sound has become?

Registers of the voice

A **register** is a range of notes which resonate in a particular area of the body. Singers usually talk about having three different registers where they 'feel' different notes:

- Notes in the **chest register** (or **chest voice**) are in the lower part of your voice. You feel the vibrations in your chest. Your speaking voice is also in this register.

- Notes in the **middle register** are in the middle part of your voice. The vibrations can be felt in the lower or upper parts of the mouth.

- Notes in the **head register** (or **head voice**) are in the upper range of your voice. You may feel the vibrations for these notes in the middle and upper parts of your head.

Hum notes in different ranges of your voice to feel where they vibrate in different parts of your upper body.

Sing a few low notes and decide where they vibrate most. Mark this place on the diagram on the right.

Then do this for a few notes in the middle and upper parts of your voice, marking these on the diagram too. You could use different colours, or write the words 'low', 'medium' and 'high'.

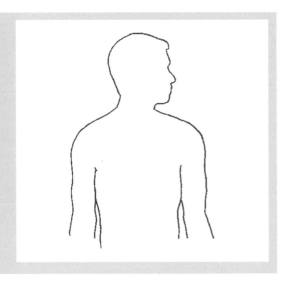

Placing your voice

Much of good singing is remembering how and where sounds vibrate and resonate inside you, and learning how to reproduce this each time you sing. When you find a good resonant sound, try hard to remember the physical sensation of making it.

Thinking about register is one way to do this. Another is 'placing' the voice. Think of your face as having different levels or areas, and imagine placing notes there as you sing. This makes it easier to make the same sound again, and to control your tone.

Moving smoothly between registers

To sing well, you need to be able to move smoothly between the registers of your voice so that the sound doesn't change suddenly as you move from one to the other. Use the following exercises to practise moving between them.

Slides and sirens

Starting on a note low in your range, make a sliding siren sound. Slide from the lower note to the higher note and back again. Start by using slides of three notes wide, and gradually extend these towards an octave. Make sure that the tone is even and the notes are connected smoothly.

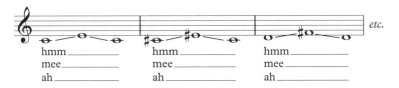

hmm _____   hmm _____   hmm _____
mee _____   mee _____   mee _____
ah _____   ah _____   ah _____

Placing the voice (1)

Sing the exercise below, starting on a note in the middle of your range. Sing slowly and steadily, breathing in between each note and placing it carefully.

Think of the area of your face where you will feel the vibrations, and widen the throat as you sing through each note. Sing the exercise several times, starting a semitone higher each time.

Placing the voice (2)

For the exercise below, choose a starting note that is fairly high in your range. Place the sound in your forehead and allow it to travel upwards as the pitch gets higher, but don't force the sound. If it feels uncomfortable, stop the exercise and ask your choir trainer to find you a different starting note.

Try to keep a light quality in the sound. To do this, you could try putting your arms out in front of you with your hands together, and drawing your hands apart slowly as you sing the exercise.

Moving between registers (1)

For the next exercise, choose a starting note that is fairly low in your range. With your hands, imagine you are drawing a circle on each side of your head, moving from the back of your head, up and over towards your face and back round. Do this while you sing the exercise. This will help you travel from one register to another with no bumps in the sound.

Moving between registers (2)

Choose a comfortable starting note for the following exercise. Place the lower notes around the lower teeth and the high notes in the forehead. Think as quickly as you can about these changes of position. However, take care not to disconnect the notes from one another – there should not be a bump or a complete change of tone.

Try sliding between the notes first. Once you can smoothly connect the notes, sing the exercise again without the slide, but keeping the sense of connection between the notes.

Agility in the voice (1)

For this exercise, make sure your vowel sounds are resonant. Don't allow the energy to collapse once you have sung the highest note: continue it through to the end of the phrase. Imagine inflating a tyre around the base of your back. This should give you the supporting muscular energy that you need.

soh	pah	soh	pah	soh		soh	pah	soh	pah	soh		soh	pah	soh	pah	so
yah	yah	yah	yah	yah		yah	yah	yah	yah	yah		yah	yah	yah	yah	yah

Agility in the voice (2)

Choose a comfortable starting note for the next exercise. Sing it several times, starting a semitone higher each time. Sing with good vowel sounds and lots of agility.

ah_____ eh_____ aw_____ ee_____ ah_____ eh_____ aw_____ ee

The nasal twang

To increase the strength of the notes in your lower register without damaging your voice, you can use a nasal 'twang' sound. Try the exercises below:

Starting on a note in the middle of your range, sing 'qua' down a scale, with a nasal twang sound. (Imagine you are about to sing the word 'quack'.) Notice that the mouth is quite closed for this sound. Then loosen your jaw and try to get the same buzz to the sound. Repeat the exercise, starting a semitone lower.

qua	qua	qua	qua	qua	qua	qua	qua	qua	qua	qua	qua	qua	qua	qua	qua

The nasal twang in the low register

As you pause on the final note of the next exercise, drop your jaw. Make sure the sound does not change as you do this. Watch yourself in the mirror. Note how the position of your face changes from being wide and open to long and relaxed.

qua	qua	quack	qua	qua	quack	qua	qua	quack

Producing an open sound in the low register

Although the nasal twang is a useful way to develop the strength of the lower register, singers should not use this sound in all their singing. Particularly during classical and choral singing, singers should aim for a sound that is open and less nasal. This exercise will help you to produce this.

Allow the jaw to drop open on 'yah', remembering the feeling you had on the last note of the previous exercise.

mee	moh	yah	mee	moh	yah	mee	moh	yah

Your job as a singer is to communicate the words and the music to your listeners. This means that your diction has to be clear – the consonants need to be precise and the vowel sounds as pure as possible.

Tongue twisters

 When you sing, you have to work much harder to produce clear words than when you are speaking. To get your tongue moving during your practice at home, try some tongue twisters like the ones on the right.

> She sells sea shells on the sea shore
>
> Copper–bottomed coffee pot
>
> The six thin things, the six thick things
>
> Red lorry, yellow lorry

 Think of a tongue twister of your own, write it here, and practise singing it.

Projecting consonants

 Imagine you are in a big hall or a church. Choose a song or hymn and whisper the words with enough energy that someone could hear you from the other side of the room. Next, sing the song very quietly, but make the consonants loud and clear.

Try to remember the amount of energy you have used to produce clear consonants and aim to sing like this every time.

Smooth lines

 If you make consonants too strong, they will interrupt the line of the phrase. To practise singing *legato* (smoothly), sing a phrase on a single vowel several times, until you can sing it smoothly. Then sing it with the words, but try to keep the line as smooth as when you sang it on the vowel.

Moving between vowels and consonants

 Use the words in the box, or your own list of words with consonants at the start and the end. Practise singing each of these words on one note in the middle of your range. Make the consonants short and the vowels long. How resonant can you make each vowel?

Loop	L	oo	p
Need	N	ee	d
Blend	Bl	eh	nd
Lark	L	ah	k
Lord	L	aw	d

Strength of consonants

 Using the list of words above or some of your own, try these experiments with consonants. (Remember to keep the vowels resonant.) Sing each word:

- quietly, with the consonants clear but not very loud
- loudly, with the consonants clear but not loud

- quietly, with the consonants as loud as you can
- loudly, with the consonants as loud as you can

 The relationship between the volume of consonants and the volume of vowels depends on the style of music. Try listening to a recording of yourself. Does the volume of vowels and consonants sound right? If you are not sure, ask your choir trainer.

Performance

As part of Red level, you must sing a short solo or solo line (which you have prepared in advance) in a service, concert or other public event. With your choir trainer, choose the solo you plan to sing and arrange where and when you will sing it.

Write the name of the solo here:

When and where will you be performing this?

Preparing your solo

When you perform your solo, your choir trainer will be listening for the following:

- Clear diction and projection, without interrupting the line of the melody

- Good breath control, with breaths being taken at appropriate points

- Even tone and the ability to move smoothly between different registers

- Good intonation (tuning) throughout, (even when singing unaccompanied)

Here are some hints to help you prepare your solo:

- Practise your solo at home. If you know it very well, you will be more confident in your performance.

- Practise your solo with and without accompaniment. This will help you learn all the notes accurately.

Listen carefully to yourself as you practise. Ask yourself the following questions. You will not be ready to give your performance until you can tick all the boxes:

- ☐ Have I learnt all the notes accurately?
- ☐ Am I making all the words clear?
- ☐ Am I singing with clear consonants, while keeping the melody smooth?
- ☐ Is my tuning good?
- ☐ Is my breathing good?
- ☐ Is my throat staying relaxed?

- ☐ Am I breathing in appropriate places?
- ☐ Am I using any dynamics?
- ☐ Will I be heard by someone at the back of the room?
- ☐ Is my music held at the right height?
- ☐ Is my posture relaxed but stable?
- ☐ Do I look like a confident performer?

Unaccompanied singing

If any of your solo is unaccompanied, your choir trainer will want to know that you can keep going with confidence. Keep the rhythm strong and steady, and try not to speed up or slow down. Concentrate on staying at the right pitch. It helps to know the tune really well, because you will be sure about the exact size of each interval.

Your performance

When you have finished your performance, your choir trainer will give you feedback about aspects of your singing. He or she may feel you need to continue working on one particular aspect of your voice and to perform a solo again later. If so, keep practising the exercises in this book and the others that your choir trainer will introduce during rehearsals, and you will find that your singing improves.

ⓘ A staff has only five lines because the human eye can only read five closely–spaced lines at a glance. But there is a way of showing notes that are higher or lower than those on the staff – by using 'temporary' lines called **leger lines**.

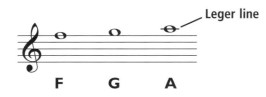

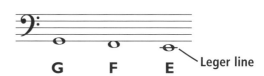

The staves on the right show the same note in the treble and bass clefs. It is often called Middle C because it sits between the two staves.

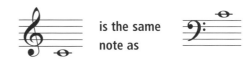

Even higher, or lower, notes can be shown by using more than one leger line, above or below the staff. Here are some leger line notes above and below the treble clef staff.

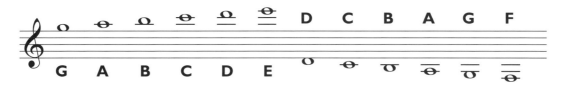

Leger lines work in the same way as the lines of the staff. After a note in a space, there's a note on a leger line, then a note in a space, and so on. Here are some leger line notes above and below the bass clef staff.

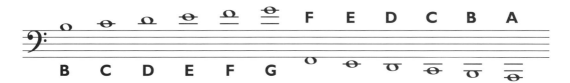

ⓘ If a piece of music has a lot of notes above or below the range of a clef, then often the composer will change the clef to avoid having to use lots of leger lines. (Music with a lot of leger lines can be more difficult to read.) For example, if a part in the bass clef had a lot of higher notes, the composer may decide to write those same notes in the treble clef instead.

 Here is a C in the treble clef. Next to it, write a C which is one octave lower.

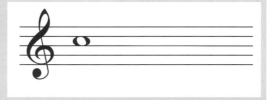

Here is a D in the bass clef. Next to it, write a D which is one octave lower, then (to the right of that) a D which is one octave higher.

Leger lines

Here is a B in the treble clef. Next to it, write a B which is one octave higher.

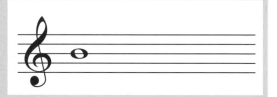

Word game
Here are some words written in leger–line notes. Can you read them?

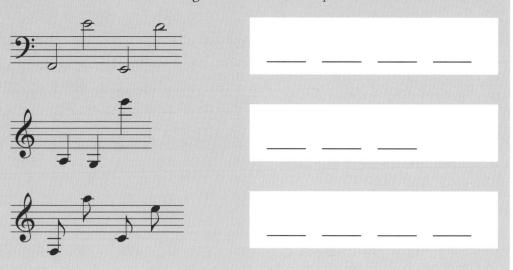

Letter box
The name of each note on the staves below is written in the letter box on the right. Match each name in the letter box to a note on the staff. (Use the notes on both clefs.)

As you match each note, cross it out in the letter box. Some letters will be left in the letter box – these spell out the name of a well–known composer. Who is it?

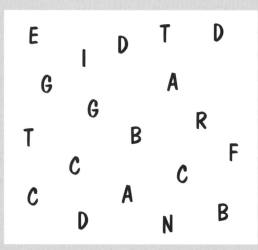

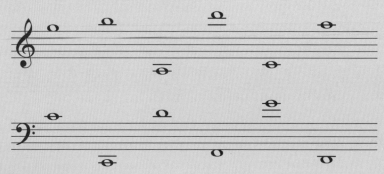

The well–known composer is:

This curved line is a slur. (See page 29 of the Dark Blue workbook or ask your choir trainer for a reminder.) A slur tells you to move smoothly between two notes of different pitches.

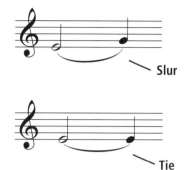

This curved line is a **tie**. It looks like a slur, but always links notes of the same pitch.

A tie tells you to treat the two notes as if they were one longer note. You add together the lengths of the two notes, and this is the length of the longer note.

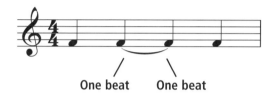

These one–beat notes are tied or 'added together' to make one longer note of two beats. You don't sing two separate one–beat notes: you make a two–beat note by holding the first note for two beats.

Ties are often used where one note is at the end of a bar and the other is at the beginning of the next. So they often cross a barline.

These two notes
become one note
lasting three beats.

 Add two ties to this example, joining notes of the same pitch.

 Look at the three ties in the music below, and answer the questions.

How many crotchet beats does tie 1 last?

How many quavers in tie 2?

How many quavers in tie 3?

If you need help with this, ask your choir trainer.

Compound time signatures

 You already know the time signatures on the right. They are often called **simple** time signatures, because the beat can be divided into two. In 2/4, 3/4 and 4/4 the beat is a crotchet, which can be divided into two quavers. The beat in 2/2 is a minim, which can be divided into two crotchets.

1 beat = 1 crotchet

1 beat = 1 minim

The time signature on the right means there are six quavers in a bar. The 8 represents a quaver. The 6 means there are six of them in a bar. The six quavers are grouped into two beats, so each beat feels as if it is divided into three.

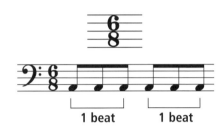

1 beat   1 beat

 Three quavers make one dotted crotchet, so in this time signature, one beat is one dotted crotchet.

1 beat = 1 dotted crotchet

 Clap some bars of six quavers. Make the first quaver of each beat stronger so that you can feel two beats in a bar. (Ask your choir trainer for help with this.)

This time signature is known as a **compound** time signature, because its beat is divided into three. Here are some more compound time signatures. For each of them, a beat is a dotted crotchet.

3 quavers in a bar	9 quavers in a bar	12 quavers in a bar
1 beat in a bar	3 beats in a bar	4 beats in a bar

 Write the time signature for music that has four dotted crotchet beats in a bar.

Write the time signature for music that has three dotted crotchet beats in a bar.

 In a piece with this time signature, how many quavers are there in a bar?

Draw one note that lasts for one dotted crotchet beat.

A **major sixth** is the interval between the first and sixth notes of a major scale. In the scale of D major, D is the first note and B is the sixth note.

Major sixth

Major sixth

A **minor sixth** is the interval between the first and sixth notes of a harmonic minor scale. (For more about harmonic minor scales, see page 20 of the Dark Blue workbook.) In the scale of D minor, D is the first note and B flat is the sixth note.

Minor sixth

Minor sixth

 Sing both of these intervals. Can you hear the difference? Which interval is larger?

Major sixth

On the staff on the left, write a note that is a major sixth higher than the one shown.

On the staff on the right, write a note that is a minor sixth higher than the one shown.

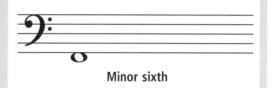

Minor sixth

 Think of a tune that begins with a major sixth and one that begins with a minor sixth. Write their names here.

Major sixth

Minor sixth

 This interval is a tone. It is also known as a **major second**.

Major second

Major second

This interval is a semitone. It is also known as a **minor second**.

Minor second

Minor second

 Sing these intervals. Can you hear the difference? Which is larger?

 How many minor seconds are there in a major second?

Intervals

 Major versions of intervals are always larger than minor versions. When talking about intervals, **major** means **larger.**

 On the staff on the right, write a note that is a major second higher than the one shown. Sing these notes at an octave that is comfortable for you.

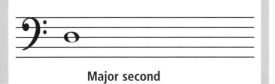

Major second

On the staff on the left, write a note that is a minor second higher than the one shown. Sing these notes at an octave that is comfortable for you.

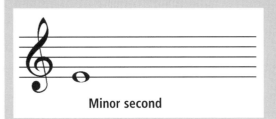

Minor second

 Think of a tune that begins with a major second and one that begins with a minor second. Write their names here.

Major second

Minor second

 This interval is a **major seventh**. It is a large interval, almost as large as an octave. When trying to imagine or sing a major seventh, it may help you to remember that it is one semitone smaller than an octave.

Major seventh

Major seventh

An octave minus a semitone equals a major seventh

 Sing D, followed by the D an octave higher, then C sharp (as below). Then try singing a major seventh from the low D directly to the C sharp, leaving out the high D.

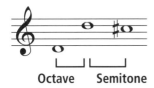

Octave   Semitone

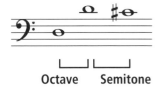

Octave   Semitone

 How many semitones are there in a major seventh?

Which note is a major seventh higher than C?

This interval is a **minor seventh**. It is one tone smaller than an octave. So it is also one semitone smaller than a major seventh.

Minor seventh

Minor seventh

An octave minus a tone
equals a minor seventh

 Sing some minor sevenths. Then sing some major sevenths to compare the two intervals.

 On the staff on the right, write a note that is a major seventh higher than the one shown. Sing this interval at a comfortable octave.

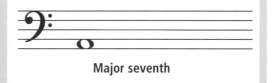

Major seventh

On the staff on the left, write a note that is a minor seventh higher than the one shown. Sing this interval at a comfortable octave.

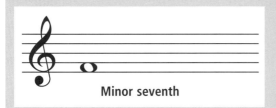

Minor seventh

 With your choir or in a group, think of a tune that contains a major seventh or one that contains an octave leap upwards followed by a semitone downwards. Then think of a tune that contains a minor seventh (or an octave leap upwards followed by a tone downwards). Write the names of the tunes here.

Major seventh

Minor seventh

 Link these intervals in order of size. Start with the smallest.

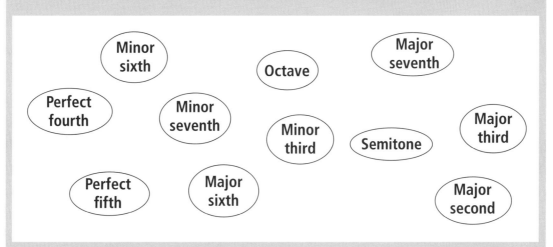

New keys and key signatures

(i) Here is a new key signature:

This is the key signature of **E major** and **C sharp minor**. Music with this key signature has four sharps.

(✎) Name the four sharps in this key signature.

_____ sharp   _____ sharp   _____ sharp   _____ sharp

(i) The keys of **A flat major** and **F minor** are related. Can you work out which sharps or flats are in their key signature? Find the key note for A flat and sing the scale. (If you have trouble singing the full octave, start on a comfortable A flat and sing up five notes to E flat. Then sing back down to A flat. Continue downwards to the E flat below, then back up to the A flat.)

(✎) Now fill in the stairs chart below for A flat major. (For a reminder about stairs charts, see the Light Blue or Dark Blue workbooks.) Put the tonic note on the top and bottom stairs, and then fill in the other notes of the scale, working out the tones and semitones as you go. Write the notes on the stave too. Remember that key signatures have *either* sharps *or* flats, not both.

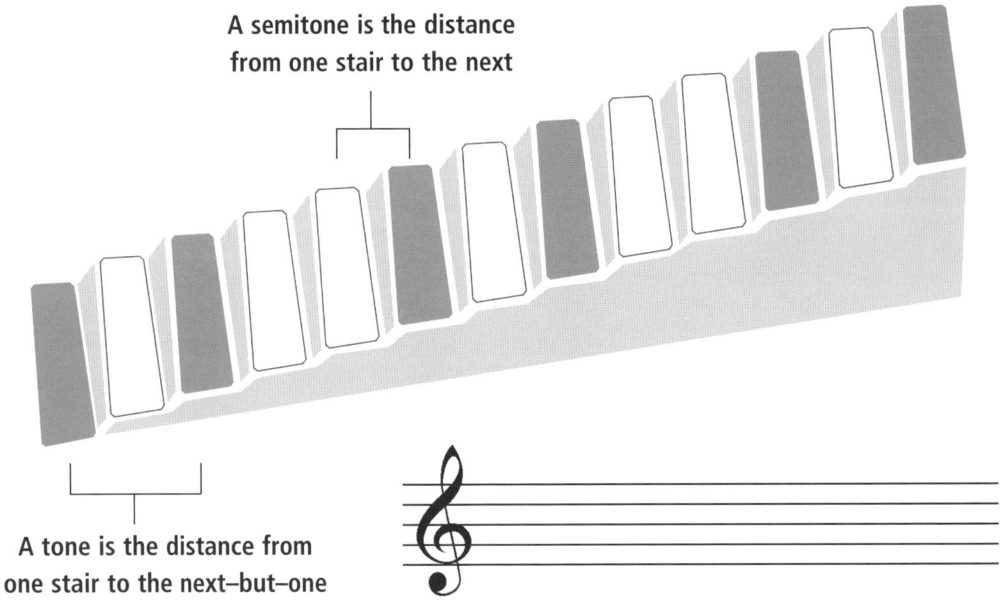

A semitone is the distance from one stair to the next

A tone is the distance from one stair to the next–but–one

(✎) How many sharps or flats are there in the key signature for A flat major and F minor?

_____ sharp(s)   _____ flat(s)

(✎) Draw a treble or bass clef on this stave and then write the key signature for A flat major and F minor. (See page 26 or ask your choir trainer for help.)

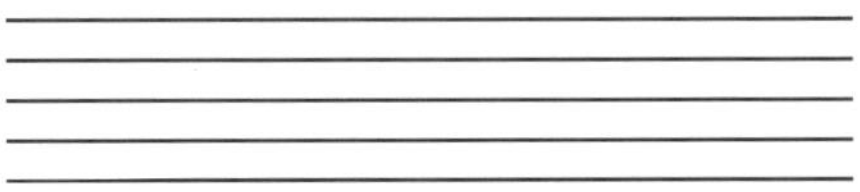

New keys and key signatures

(i) Here is another new key signature:

This is the key signature of **B major**. Music with this key signature has five sharps: F, C, G, D and A sharps.

What is the relative minor key of B major? (For a reminder about related keys, see pages 22–23 of the Dark Blue book or ask your choir trainer.)

_____ minor

Sing a scale of B major, ascending (going up) and descending (going down). Then sing a scale of its relative minor key.

(i) When you see a key signature with more than one flat, remember this easy way of identifying its major key. Look at the second–to–last flat. This is the key signature's major key.

In this example, there are five flats. The second–to–last flat is D flat, so this is the key signature of **D flat major**. (It is also the key signature of **B flat minor.**)

Name the five flats in the key signature above.

_____ flat

_____ flat

_____ flat

_____ flat

_____ flat

Here is a key signature of three flats. What is the name of its major key?

_____ major

Write a clef on this staff and then write the key signature for B minor and D major.

Which two keys have a key signature of four sharps?

_____ major

_____ minor

Writing key signatures

In key signatures, each sharp and flat has its own position on the staff. The staves on the right show the positions of sharps and flats in key signatures.

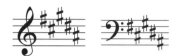

  Positions for F, C, G, D and A sharps in treble and bass clefs

Positions for B, E, A, D and G flats in treble and bass clefs

 Key signatures puzzle

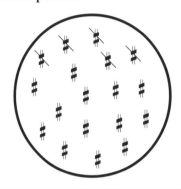 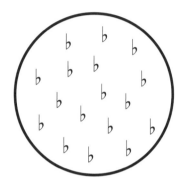

On the staves below, write the key signature of each key using only the sharps and flats in the circles above. Remember to draw a clef before each key signature. As you use each sharp or flat, cross it out in the circle. The first one is done for you.

G♯ minor	A♭ major	E major	G minor

A major	B♭ minor	C minor	E minor

When you have finished, there will be some sharps and flats left over. Make them into key signatures by writing them on the staves on the right. (Draw a clef on each staff first.)

Sharps

Flats

Each of these two key signatures that you have written is for a major key and its relative minor key. Write the names of the keys in the box on the left.

Sharps

____ major and ____ minor

Flats

____ major and ____ minor

An **arpeggio** (say 'ar – pedgie – oh') is a pattern of notes that is made when you play the notes of a chord separately. A **major arpeggio** contains the first, third and fifth notes of a major scale. A **minor arpeggio** contains the first, third and fifth notes of a minor scale.

These are the same notes that form a triad (see page 26 of the Dark Blue workbook). A triad is a chord, which means that the notes are sounded together. In an arpeggio, the notes are played one at a time, usually in order, either upwards or downwards.

G major triad   G major arpeggio

Often, an arpeggio also includes the tonic an octave higher.

**G major arpeggio ascending (going up)
and then descending (going down)**

G minor arpeggio ascending and descending

Sing some major and minor arpeggios (ascending and descending).

Name the first, third and fifth notes in the scale of A major.	First: Third: Fifth:

	Put a clef on this staff, then write an arpeggio of A major, ascending. Start with the tonic, then write the third and fifth notes, then write the tonic an octave higher. One of the notes will need an accidental.

Put a clef on this staff, then write the key signature of A major. Then write the arpeggio, as you have done above. This time you will not need the accidental.	

Performance instructions

 You will find many different kinds of instructions in your printed music that give you clues as to how it should be sung. These instructions are usually in Italian. Sometimes they are shortened versions of Italian words.

Here are some general instructions:

a cappella	without accompaniment
divisi (or *div.*) (say 'div–ezy')	divide into two or more groups
tutti (say 'tu–tee')	all, everybody
molto	much, very
poco (say 'poh–koh')	a little
semplice (say 'semp–lee–chey')	simple, simply
sempre (say 'sem–pray')	always
subito (or *sub.*) (say 'soo–be–toh')	suddenly

 Here are some instructions relating to speed (or tempo):

a tempo	back to the previous speed
tempo primo (say 'pree–moh')	back to the original speed
stringendo (or *string.*)	getting faster
allargando (or *allarg.*)	broadening out, getting slower
largo	slow and broad
larghetto (say 'lar–get–toh')	slow (but less slow than *largo*)
mosso	movement
più mosso (say 'pyoo')	more movement
meno mosso (say 'meh–noh')	less movement
rubato (say 'roo–bah–toh')	with freedom of time (slowing and quickening freely)

 These instructions tell you about the character of the music:

vivace (say 'viv–ah–chey')	lively
maestoso (say 'my–stoh–soh')	majestically
dolce (say 'dol – chey')	sweetly
espressivo	with expression
cantabile (say 'can–ta–be–ley')	in a singing style
sostenuto	sustained
tenuto (say 'teh–new–toh')	held on
forzando (say 'fort–san–doh') (or *fz*)	forcing, accented
sforzando (say 'sfort–san–doh') (or *sfz*)	sudden accent

Performance instructions

These instructions tell you about sudden changes in dynamic:

subito piano (or *sub. p*) suddenly quiet

forte piano (or *fp*) loud, then immediately quiet

Write the instruction for 'getting faster'.

Write the instruction which tells you to go back to the original speed.

Write the Italian word which tells you to sing with expression.

What is the Italian for 'sweetly'?

Write the instruction for 'suddenly loud'.

What is the Italian for 'very lively'?

Write the instruction for 'getting slower'.

What is the Italian for 'a little'?

 Sing some scales, arpeggios or vocal exercises to practise the following:

sforzando *subito piano*

a tempo

dolce *allargando*

forte piano *subito forte*

stringendo

espressivo *forzando*

Understanding the music we sing

 As a performer, you have to communicate the meaning of each piece you sing. To do this, you must understand the words and background of the music. For your Red level 'Repertoire' target (see page 42), you have to collect some information about pieces that you sing in your choir. The worksheet opposite shows the type of questions you need to answer for each piece. If you are unsure where to find out about music and composers, talk to your choir trainer.

 Putting the information together
Make copies of the worksheet opposite so that you can do this activity with several pieces. With your choir trainer, choose a piece you have learned with your choir and fill in a worksheet for it. Gather as much information as you can – you may want to make notes on a separate sheet too. When you have collected your information, use it to write some programme notes (see page 32).

 Hints and tips
Here are a few useful things to bear in mind:

- For some pieces, you may not find an answer to every question. For example, it's not always possible to name the composer – the music may be anonymous or traditional. But you may find other details, such as the name of the arranger.

- If the author of a text is unknown, look for other facts about it, such as when or where it was written. Is it a poem, a prayer, part of the Bible?

- Was the piece composed for a particular event, or written with a group of people or a soloist in mind?

- Are there any interesting facts about the life of the composer?

- Think about how the music, the text and the mood of the piece are linked. Use your knowledge of music theory knowledge to help you with this (for example, time signature, key, tempo, number of parts, etc.).

 Infoquest
Do some research about the five choral composers below and match the names to the facts. The first letters of each name will spell the surname of another composer. Find the full name and dates of that composer.

LEIGHTON	TALLIS	STAINER	HAYDN	OUSELEY

_____ wrote 104 symphonies.

_____ was born in 1825.

_____ died in 1988.

_____ wrote *The Crucifixion*.

_____ wrote a 40-part motet.

The hidden composer's name is:	The hidden composer lived from:
	_____ to _____

Understanding the music we sing

Name the piece of music.

Name the composer.

Where do the words come from?

Give the composer's dates of birth and death.

What country did he or she live in?

When is the piece normally sung? At a particular time of year or for a particular event?

What century or musical period was the composer writing in?

Name some other pieces by this composer.

What key is the piece in?

Give the time signature of the piece.

Name some other composers who wrote in the same period.

What is the mood of the music?

Give any interesting information about the composer (for example, job, family, and so on) or the piece (for example, where it was first performed)

Writing programme notes

Concert programme booklets often contain **programme notes** – information to tell listeners about the music. For Red level, you have to write some programme notes using the information you collected for the worksheet on the previous page. Make copies of this page so that you can repeat it with several pieces of music.

Make your notes clear, easy to read, and interesting. Think about what your listeners would want to know. If you went to a concert and bought a programme, what kind of information would you like to have about the music? The following additional information might be useful:

- What is the text about? Explain it in your own words. (Is it in English? If not, your readers need to know what language it is in and what it means.)

- Describe the music. How many vocal parts are there? What instruments are used? What is the feeling or mood of the music? Why does it feel like this?

Name the piece of music.

Programme note:

You may want to continue writing on a separate piece of paper.

Singing as part of a choir

 As a singer, you need to practise individually and work on your own voice and musical ability in order to improve. You can also improve your skills as a choir member. At Red level, you are able to take more responsibility within the choir and lead the less experienced singers. This is rather like being a captain of a sports team; you are expected to play to the best of your ability, but you also have the added responsibility of leading your team members to do the best they can.

The team manager relies on the captain to do this important job. In a similar way, your choir trainer relies on you to do this within your choir. You provide a lead to your team members by setting a good example with your attendance, your singing and your behaviour in rehearsals and services or concerts. Your choir trainer needs to know that you:

- are committed, reliable and punctual. This means your attendance record is very good. You can always be relied on to arrive on time and to sing to the best of your ability.

- understand the difference between solo and choral singing. This means you are able to sing solos confidently, and you are also able to give a lead to choir members while blending your voice with them.

- will always inform him or her in advance if you are not able to attend a rehearsal or performance.

- will help less experienced singers without making a fuss. This might involve helping a singer to find the right piece of music or the right page during a rehearsal, or making sure that they know what time to attend, or what to wear, and so on.

 Ask yourself the following questions, write the answers here, then ask your choir trainer to comment.

Is my attendance record good? Could it be improved?

Do I help the less experienced members of my choir? Could I be more helpful?

Do I set an example by my behaviour and my singing?

Do I understand the difference between solo and choral singing? (Think of one difference and write it here.)

Choir in context

 This module of *Voice for Life* is about what it means to sing in a choir and what your choir means to you, other choir members, and the people who listen to it. As the answers to these things are different for each choir and singer, there are no formal tests for this module.

Instead, your choir trainer will ask you to think about the topics in this section of the book, one at a time, and write your answers to the questions in the boxes. (You may be asked to work in a group with other singers.) You will be given plenty of time to work on each topic, so work through the questions carefully one by one. Before you start writing, it may help to talk to other singers or do some Internet research.

Your choir trainer will look at your answers and may chat with you about them. You may be asked to follow up some points or answer more questions. When the topic is completed, he or she will sign the box in the targets on page 43. To complete this module for Red level, you have to finish at least *one* of the topics, but your choir trainer may want you to do more. Topic 3 is for church choirs only.

 Topic 1: The wider community
Your choir isn't only important to the people who sing in it. It affects the people who listen to it too. Depending on the context of the choir, these may be: your church congregation, your school, your concert audiences and so on. The aim of this topic is to find out how your choir operates within your community.

To do this, interview at least three members of your choir's wider community – anyone who is affected by it but who doesn't sing in it. They could be members of your choir's audience or congregation, or people who help to run it. Talk to your choir trainer, who will help you to organize this. You can do your interviews on your own or, if you will feel more comfortable, ask another singer to help you.

In the worksheet opposite, there are five questions to ask in the upper box. If you like, add a sixth question of your own. Then take some copies to do your interviews. Find three people to interview and write their names in the box below.

 When you do your interviews, write the responses in the spaces on your copies. Think about the replies, and answer the following questions:

- Did people reply in the way you expected?

- How did you feel about the replies?

- What benefits does the choir bring to the community?

- Do the replies suggest ways to change what the choir does to serve its community better?

Now write your conclusions in the lower box on the opposite page, and share them with your choir trainer. (Use extra paper if you need to.)

1) What contact do you have with the choir?

2) What do you expect from the choir?

3) Does the choir meet your expectations?

4) How are you affected by the choir's singing?

5) How could the choir contribute more to the wider community?

6)

Your conclusions

You may photocopy this page

Choir in context

Topic 2: The roots of our choir

The aim of this topic is to encourage you to explore the history of your choir – to find out about how it began, to think about how it has changed, and to look at your choir as an organization with a past, a present and a future. Knowing a bit about our history can help us to understand who we are. This is true for individual people and for organizations such as choirs and schools too.

Before you start this topic, think a bit about yourself, your family and its history. Does your family name reveal anything about your background or origins? If you wanted to know about the history of your family, who would you ask? Now think about your choir in the same way. Can you tell anything about it from its name? And where would you go to find out about its history? Who would you ask?

To complete this topic, you need to collect information about the origins of your choir. (Don't worry if your choir is quite new – it still has a history.) To do this you will need to decide on your sources – where to find the information. Are there people to ask (other singers, or members of your audience or congregation), or documents or websites to look at? Does your choir have a diary or archive you could consult? Talk to your choir trainer about this, or other senior members of your choir.

In the box below, list *three* sources you can use for information about the history of your choir.

Make copies of the worksheet on the opposite page, and consult each of your sources by asking the questions in the boxes. You may not get an answer to every question from every source, but when you have all the answers, put the information together by writing it into the boxes opposite. (Don't worry if you can't find the answers to all the questions. If you find any other interesting facts, include those too. For example, has the choir given any important performances? Won any competitions? Had any famous members? Travelled far?)

The answers you write opposite will form a short history of your choir. Your choir trainer will discuss the results of your research with you. He or she may ask you more questions about what you have written, or ask you to find some extra information. You may be asked to give a short presentation to other choir members, or write a brief article (to go into a concert programme for example).

Who founded the choir? When?

Why was it set up?

How many were in the choir at the beginning? And what voice parts?

What were its original activities, pattern and place of meeting?

What was its name? How was this chosen?

What do you know about the music sung by the choir at the beginning?

How has the choir changed since it was founded?

Are there any other interesting facts about the choir?

Choir in context

Topic 3: Music in worship

In this topic, you will explore the links between music and prayer, and how music helps individuals and congregations to worship. (This topic follows on from topic 3 in Module E of the Dark Blue workbook – 'Festivals in the Christian Year' – so it may be useful to review that before you start.)

Think about a regular church service with which you are familiar (such as Eucharist/Communion or Morning Prayer). It could be one in which your choir takes part, or one at a church you attend. Think about the structure of this service, and answer the questions in the box below. (Refer to a service book or card if you like.)

Write the name of the service you have chosen.

List the different parts of the service. In brackets after each part, say whether it is spoken or sung.

What role does music play in this service?

Are some parts sung by the choir alone?

Does the congregation join in with the music? How?

Now think about texts that are regularly sung in services that are familiar to you – for example *Kyrie eleison, Glory to God, Holy holy holy, Lamb of God, Magnificat* or any other sung text from the service you choose. For *two* of these texts, write their names in the box below and briefly describe their origins, in the Bible or elsewhere. This may require some research.

Text 1

Text 2

Now think about the music that you have heard or sung in services recently. Choose one of your favourites, write its name in the box below, then answer the questions about it.

The title and composer of the piece:

Give the context of the piece in the service. Is it for a particular festival or occasion?

How is the congregation affected by this piece? How does the music help prayer and reflection?

Think of an appropriate prayer and Bible reading to go with this piece.

Targets

The targets for the Red level of *Voice for Life* are listed on pages 40–43. As you work through this book, you will learn to do all the things below. This section is a record of your progress, so write your name here.

_____

Each time you achieve a target, your choir trainer will sign the box and record the date. There is no time limit to complete the targets. It is more important to learn everything thoroughly than to rush to finish the book. Your choir trainer will make sure that you make steady progress so that when you finish the book you are prepared for the next level.

When all the boxes are signed, you have successfully completed Red level. Your choir trainer will sign the declaration on the inside back cover of this book, where you can also find out what happens next.

Module A: Using the voice well
The singer understands the need for regular practice and:

	Signed:	Date:
• understands the need for good posture; as second nature, consistently stands and sits well in rehearsals and performances.		
• understands the basic mechanics of breathing.		
• has developed good breath management and demonstrates this through a good even tone and control of dynamics.		
• understands where it is appropriate to breathe in the music, and why, and understands how to achieve the effect of no breathing in a piece or phrase using staggered breathing as part of the choir.		
• understands the basic mechanics of sound production.		
• understands the different registers of the voice and how to access them.		
• has developed the range and resonance of the voice, and has demonstrated this by singing an ascending and descending scale of at least an octave on any vowel, with resonance throughout, being aware of placing the sounds correctly and avoiding a break in the resonance.		

Module A *continued*

The singer:

	Signed:	Date:
• understands the need for clear diction and how to use diction appropriately according to the style of music being performed, and demonstrates this in rehearsals and performances.		
• understands the difference between solo and choral singing and contributes to the overall sound whilst blending the voice with the ensemble as a whole.		
• has sung accurately and musically a carefully prepared short solo or solo line in a service, concert or similar public event.		

Module B: Musical skills and understanding

The singer has completed the theory section of the Red workbook and demonstrates that he/she knows and understands:

	Signed:	Date:
• the names of pitches in the treble and bass clefs, including those on leger lines.		
• time values of notes and rests, including tied notes.		
• key signatures up to five sharps and flats (major & minor).		
• compound time signatures.		
• the characteristics and names of major, minor and perfect intervals up to an octave.		
• the notes of major and minor arpeggios in keys of up to five sharps and flats.		
• the frequently used performance directions listed on page 28 and 29.		

Module B *continued*

The singer has read and understood the music theory in Module B and can:

	Signed:	Date:
• sing back a melody. The key chord and key note will first be sounded and the pulse indicated. The melody will be played twice.		
• sing a one–octave major or minor arpeggio, unaccompanied, ascending and descending. The key chord and note will first be indicated.		

Module B *continued*

The singer has read and understood the music theory in Module B and can:

	Signed:	Date:

- look at a short excerpt of music and:
  i) name the key (major or minor);
  ii) name the pitch of any note in the first
  chord; and iii) on hearing the first chord,
  can sing any of its notes in their vocal
  range at the request of the choir trainer.

- sing any major, minor or perfect interval up
  to an octave above a given starting note.

- tap the pulse of a passage of music in
  simple or compound time. The passage
  will be played twice and on the second
  playing the singer should tap the beat
  and stress where the strong beat falls.
  The singer should then state whether the
  passage is in 2, 3 or 4 time.

- sing from sight a simple song or anthem
  with words, with awareness of dynamics,
  phrasing and expression. The key chord
  and key note will first be sounded. The
  set piece may be in simple or compound
  time, in any key up to five sharps or flats,
  and include dotted and tied notes.

Module C: Repertoire

The singer has completed the section on repertoire in the workbook and knows
how to take a piece of music and:

	Signed:	Date:

- find out who wrote the music and when
  (e.g. which period or century).

- find the source of the text (e.g. the Bible,
  a poem, a prayer).

- discuss in simple terms the relationship
  between the music/text/mood using
  some basic musical analysis (learned
  from Module B).

- find some simple information about the
  life of the composer (e.g. family, job).

- find out whether the piece was originally
  composed for a particular event, or
  commissioned and/or written with a
  certain individual or group in mind.

- turn this information into programme
  notes.

MODULE D: Belonging to the choir
The singer:

Signed: Date:

• is committed, reliable and punctual, always informing the choir trainer before being absent.

• leads other singers by example with attendance, singing and behaviour in rehearsals and services/concerts.

• understands the difference between solo and choral singing.

• helps the less experienced singers in the choir without causing fuss or distraction.

MODULE E: Choir in context
The singer has completed at least *one* of the three topics on pages 34–39

Signed: Date:

• Topic 1: The wider community

• Topic 2: The roots of our choir

• Topic 3: Music in worship

Here, your choir trainer may write extra information, comments abour your progress, or things to remember when you move up to the next level.

Reference

On this page and the next, you can find many of the signs and symbols you will see in the music you sing. Some of them you will already know from earlier *Voice for Life* workbooks. Things that are newly explained in this book are shown below with a page number which tells you where to find a more detailed explanation.

Notes with leger lines in the treble clef   (page 17)

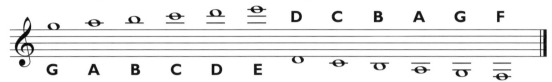

Notes with leger lines in the bass clef   (page 17)

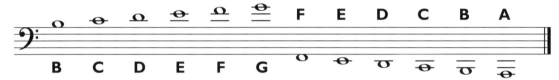

Note lengths

𝅝	Semibreve (four crotchet beats)	♩	Crotchet (one beat in a time signature where the lower number is 4)
𝅗𝅥.	Dotted minim (three crotchet beats)	♪	Quaver (half a crotchet beat)
𝅗𝅥	Minim (two crotchet beats)	𝅘𝅥𝅯	Semiquaver (a quarter of a crotchet beat)
♩.	Dotted crotchet (one–and–a–half crotchet beats)		

Rests

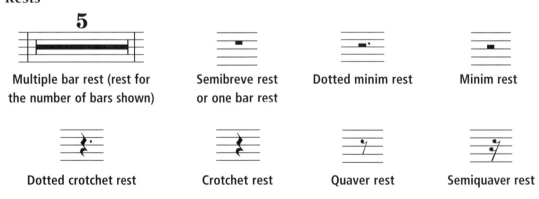

Multiple bar rest (rest for the number of bars shown)	Semibreve rest or one bar rest	Dotted minim rest	Minim rest
Dotted crotchet rest	Crotchet rest	Quaver rest	Semiquaver rest

Dynamics

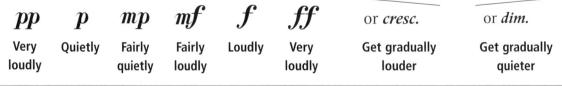

pp	*p*	*mp*	*mf*	*f*	*ff*	or *cresc.*	or *dim.*
Very loudly	Quietly	Fairly quietly	Fairly loudly	Loudly	Very loudly	Get gradually louder	Get gradually quieter

Simple time signatures

4 crotchet beats in a bar	4 crotchet beats in a bar	3 crotchet beats in a bar	2 crotchet beats in a bar	2 minim beats in a bar	2 minim beats in a bar
$\frac{4}{4}$	$\mathbf{C}$	$\frac{3}{4}$	$\frac{2}{4}$	$\frac{2}{2}$	$\mathbf{\mathvarphi}$

Compound time signatures (page 20)

In the compound time signatures shown below, each main beat is a dotted crotchet which divides into three quavers.

4 dotted crotchet beats in a bar (12 quavers)	3 dotted crotchet beats in a bar (9 quavers)	2 dotted crotchet beats in a bar (6 quavers)	1 dotted crotchet beat in a bar (3 quavers)
$\frac{12}{8}$	$\frac{9}{8}$	$\frac{6}{8}$	$\frac{3}{8}$

Key signatures

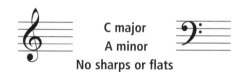

C major
A minor
No sharps or flats

G major
E minor
One sharp: F

F major
D minor
One flat: B

D major
B minor
Two sharps: F, C

B flat major
G minor
Two flats: B, E

A major
F sharp minor
Three sharps: F, C, G

E flat major
C minor
Three flats: B, E, A

E major
C sharp minor
Four sharps: F, C, G, D

A flat major
F minor
Four flats: B, E, A, D

B major
G sharp minor
Five sharps: F, C, G, D, A

D flat major
B flat minor
Five flats: B, E, A, D, G

Intervals (pages 21–23)

Here are the intervals you have learned to sing and recognise so far in *Voice for Life*, in ascending order of size, in the treble and bass clefs.

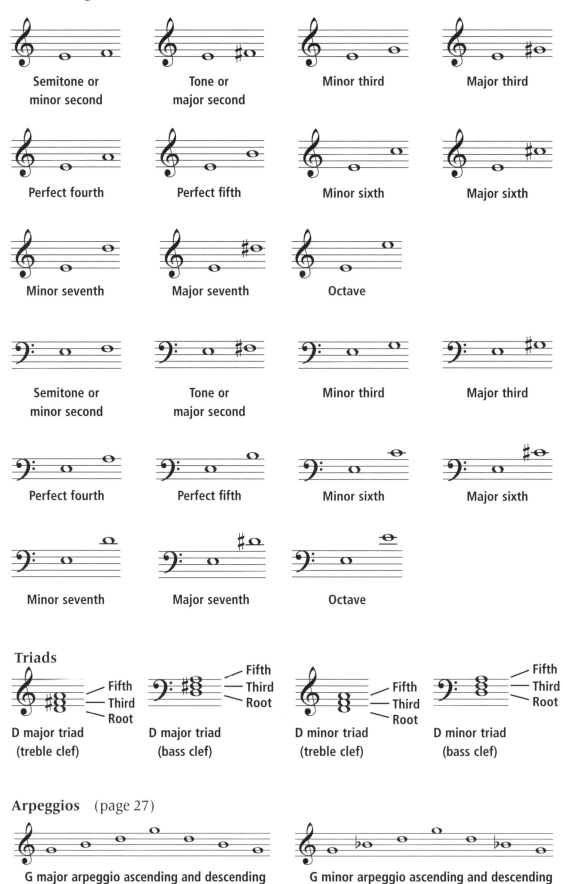

Triads

D major triad (treble clef)

D major triad (bass clef)

D minor triad (treble clef)

D minor triad (bass clef)

Arpeggios (page 27)

G major arpeggio ascending and descending

G minor arpeggio ascending and descending

Important words used in this book are explained briefly here. For a more detailed explanation, go to the pages listed under each heading. Any word in **bold** type also has an entry elswhere in this index.

Index